BALTIMORE RAVENS

TRIVIA BOOK

By Naomi Cooper

To my beloved readers,

Words can't describe how grateful I am towards your support for buying this book. You completely give me the encouragement and motivation to write other books in the future. I hope you can enjoy every page of this book and look forward to hearing from you soon!

INTRODUCTION

The Baltimore Ravens is a professional American football team based in Baltimore. The Ravens compete in the National Football League (NFL) as a member club of the American Football Conference (AFC) North division. The team plays its home games at M&T Bank Stadium and is headquartered in Owings Mill, Maryland.

If you are a die-hard fan of this awesome team and looking for anything related to it, this book – *BALTIMORE RAVENS TRIVIA BOOK*, is a perfect choice for you.

Containing a bunch of trivia questions along with fascinating facts related to the Ravens, this book promises to give you the greatest experience while learning about your favorite team. Let's get started!

Table of Contents

A. Trivia

1. Who was the first Baltimore Ravens player to make the Pro Bowl in 10 straight seasons?

   A. Ray Lewis

   B. Peter Boulware

   C. Jonathan Ogden

   D. Michael McCrary

2. In 2006, the Baltimore Ravens lost one of their last 10 games against which team?

   A. Denver Broncos

   B. Kansas City Chiefs

   C. Cleveland Browns

   D. Cincinnati Bengals

3. Who did the Baltimore Ravens take in the 2007 NFL Draft with their first round pick?

   A. Joe Staley

   B. Ben Grubbs

   C. Haloti Ngata

   D. Yamon Figurs

4. Baltimore Ravens Pro-Bowler Ray Lewis played for which college?

   A. Florida

   B. Georgia Tech

   C. Notre Dame

   D. Miami

5. Who was the first Baltimore Ravens running back to surpass 2,000 rushing yards in a single season?

   A. Earnest Byner

   B. Bam Morris

   C. Jamal Lewis

   D. Priest Holmes

6. Who was the first Baltimore Ravens quarterback to toss for 300 yards in a single game?

   A. Eric Zeier

   B. Steve McNair

   C. Elvis Grbac

   D. Vinny Testaverde

7. The Baltimore Ravens lost starter running back Jamal Lewis to which team in the 2006-07 off-season?

   A. Green Bay Packers

   B. Denver Broncos

   C. Cleveland Browns

   D. Buffalo Bills

8. The Ravens acquired which player to replace the departed Jamal Lewis during the 2006-07 off-season?

   A. Ahman Green

   B. Anthony Thomas

   C. Willis McGahee

   D. Travis Henry

9. Which number did Baltimore Raven Ray Lewis wear most seasons?

A. #50

B. #52

C. #48

D. #32

10. Which Baltimore Raven was voted the NFL Defensive Player of the Year in 2004?

A. Ray Lewis

B. Peter Boulware

C. Ed Reed

D. Terrell Suggs

11. Who was the first-round pick for the Baltimore Ravens in the 2005 NFL Draft?

A. Dan Cody

B. Dwan Edwards

C. Kyle Boller

D. Mark Clayton

12. Who was the first Baltimore Ravens player to return two punts for touchdowns in a single game?

A. B.J. Sams

B. Chris McAlister

C. Lamont Brightful

D. Jermaine Lewis

13. In what year did the Baltimore Ravens win their second AFC North Division championship?

A. 2005

B. 2006

C. 2004

D. 2003

14. Which of these teams beat the Baltimore Ravens in the 2007 season?

A. New York Jets

B. San Francisco 49ers

C. St. Louis Rams

D. Miami Dolphins

15. Which player recorded 82 solo tackles for the Baltimore Ravens in the 2007 season?

    A. Ray Lewis

    B. Dwan Edwards

    C. Bart Scott

    D. Corey Ivy

16. Ray Lewis set an NFL record by making how many tackles in one postseason?

    A. 41

    B. 61

    C. 51

    D. 31

17. Jamal Lewis set an NFL record by rushing for how many yards in a 2003 game?

    A. 275

    B. 255

    C. 315

    D. 295

18. While growing up, Terrell Suggs played football with what future MLB star?

    A. Miguel Cabrera

    B. Justin Verlander

    C. Joe Mauer

    D. Josh Hamilton

19. In 2008, Ed Reed broke his own NFL record by returning an interception how many yards?

    A. 107

    B. 104

    C. 106

    D. 105

20. What TV show did Tony Siragusa host on the DIY network?

    A. Man Machines

    B. Man Castles

    C. Man Base

    D. Man Caves

21. In high school, Tony Siragusa was a state champion in which sport?

    A. Wrestling

    B. Football

    C. Boxing

    D. Karate

22. In college, Jonathan Ogden won an NCAA title in what track & field event?

    A. Discus

    B. Hammer Throw

    C. Shot Put

    D. Javelin

23. Rod Woodson was the quarterbacks coach for which team in 2011?

    A. San Francisco 49ers

    B. Pittsburgh Steelers

    C. Oakland Raiders

    D. Baltimore Ravens

24. Haloti Ngata's parents were immigrants from what country?

    A. Trinidad & Tobago

    B. Togo

    C. Tanzania

    D. Tonga

25. Todd Heap was selected with which overall pick in the 2001 draft?

    A. 11th

    B. 41st

    C. 31st

    D. 21st

26. Todd Heap is related to what Hall of Fame quarterback?

    A. Danny White

    B. Roger Staubach

    C. Terry Bradshaw

    D. Joe Montana

27. In 2008, Peter Boulware ran for the state House of Representatives for which state?

A. Florida

B. Maryland

C. South Carolina

D. Kentucky

28. Derrick Mason set an NFL record with how many all-purpose yards in 2000?

A. 2659

B. 4211

C. 3708

D. 1944

29. Chris McAlister's father James played in the NFL at which position?

A. Center

B. Tight end

C. Punter

D. Running back

30. What is Matt Stover's real first name?

    A. Matthew

    B. John

    C. Aaron

    D. David

31. Which team originally drafted Matt Stover in 1990?

    A. Cleveland Browns

    B. Baltimore Ravens

    C. New York Giants

    D. Indianapolis Colts

32. For the 2014 Ravens, what is Brian Pariani's title?

    A. Offensive coordinator

    B. Cross training specialist

    C. Strength & conditioning coach

    D. Tight ends coach

33. Through 2006, what was the Raven's regular-season record against the Steelers with Brian Billick as their Head coach?

    A. 6-10

    B. 8-8

    C. 10-6

    D. 12-4

34. What type of aircraft performed the opening day fly-over since the team was created?

    A. A-10 Warthog

    B. F-15 Eagle

    C. F-16 Falcon

    D. F-18 Hornet

35. What is the name of the team's marching band?

    A. Baltimore Pride

    B. Marching Ravens

    C. Remember the Colt

    D. Charm City Marching Band

36. In 2000, what quarterback led the Ravens back from a 14-point deficit to beat the Jacksonville Jaguars, 39-36?

    A. Trent Dilfer

    B. Stone Casey

    C. Tony Banks

    D. Kyle Boller

37. The Ravens became the first team since the 1923 Detroit Lions to do what after beating the Cleveland Browns, 12-0?

    A. Have at least 10 sacks

    B. Have at least 5 interceptions

    C. Have at least 1 safety

    D. Post back to back shutouts

38. What former Raven was known as "Jelly Roll"?

    A. Michael McCrary

    B. Obafemi Ayanbadejo

    C. Lional Dalton

    D. Orlando Brown

39. Through 2006 how many times have the Ravens shut out the Steelers?

A. 0

B. 1

C. 2

D. 3

40. In the 2000 AFC Divisional Playoffs, Anthony Mitchell took a blocked FG how many yards for a TD?

A. 75

B. 57

C. 90

D. 62

41. Which Raven watches videos of lions hunting before each game?

A. Ed Reed

B. Kelly Gregg

C. Trevor Pryce

D. Ray Lewis

42. How many touchdowns did Jamal Lewis score in 2003?

    A. 8

    B. 10

    C. 14

    D. 16

43. What song does Ray Lewis dance too during pregame introductions?

    A. "It Wasn't Me"

    B. "Hot In Here"

    C. "Heart Of A Champion"

    D. "Back In Black"

44. During the Super Bowl year how many games did the Ravens go without scoring a touchdown?

    A. 2

    B. 5

    C. 7

    D. 10

45. Who has the nickname "Buddy Lee?"

    A. Kelly Gregg

    B. Haloti Ngata

    C. Todd Heap

    D. Justin Bannan

46. The most points put up by the Ravens all-time is 48. Against what team did they score 48 points on?

    A. Minnesota Vikings

    B. Green Bay Packers

    C. Cleveland Browns

    D. New York Jets

47. How many turnovers did the Ravens have in the two games vs the Bengals in the 2007 season?

    A. 3

    B. 8

    C. 12

    D. 15

48. Which old team of Deion Sanders did he intercept a pass against when he played here?

   A. Dallas Cowboys

   B. Washington Redskins

   C. Atlanta Falcons

   D. San Francisco 49ers

49. Who was Denver's kicker that missed the field goal Chris McAllister ran back 107 yards for a touchdown?

   A. Shayne Graham

   B. Sebastian Janikowski

   C. Jason Elam

   D. Ryan Longwell

50. Who has the second-most tackles in Ravens History?

   A. Ray Lewis

   B. Peter Boulware

   C. Bart Scott

   D. Kelly Gregg

51. Which Ravens player set the NFL record for interception return yards in 2012?

A. Ray Rice

B. Ray Lewis

C. Dennis Pitta

D. Ed Reed

52. Which Ravens quarterback was sacked 35 times during the 2012 season?

A. Tyrod Taylor

B. Joe Flacco

C. David Reed

D. Anthony Allen

53. Which Ravens running back made his third straight Pro Bowl in 2012?

A. Anthony Allen

B. Bernard Pierce

C. Torrey Smith

D. Ray Rice

54. Who led the Ravens in tackles for the 2012 season?

A. Joe Flacco

B. LaQuan Williams

C. Bernard Pollard

D. Jacoby Jones

55. Which 14-year veteran started every game at center for the Ravens in 2012?

A. Billy Bajema

B. Kelechi Osemele

C. Vonta Leach

D. Matt Birk

56. In Jamal Lewis' record-breaking 2003 season, how many rushing yards did he get in the opener against Pittsburgh?

A. 51

B. 118

C. 142

D. 69

57. Joe Flacco won a Super Bowl MVP for his performance against which team in 2013?

A. Green Bay Packers

B. New York Giants

C. San Francisco 49ers

D. New Orleans Saints

58. Whose record did Joe Flacco tie for most postseason touchdowns in a career?

A. Aaron Rodgers

B. Joe Montana

C. Ben Roethlisberger

D. Eli Manning

59. Marshal Yanda has played which two positions in his first six years in the NFL?

A. Running Back and Fullback

B. Guard and Tackle

C. Safety and Cornerback

D. Wide Receiver and Tight End

60. Marshal Yanda blocked for which running back when he led the league in yards from scrimmage?

    A. Jamal Lewis

    B. Franco Harris

    C. Jim Brown

    D. Ray Rice

61. In their 2003 win over Seattle, the Ravens set a team record for overcoming how large a fourth-quarter deficit?

    A. 17 Points

    B. 24 Points

    C. 21 Points

    D. 20 Points

62. Ray Lewis was the second linebacker to win_____?

    A. NFL MVP

    B. Defensive Player of the Year

    C. Super Bowl MVP

    D. Defensive Rookie of the Year

63. During his rookie year, Jamal Lewis led the Ravens to a Super Bowl victory over which team?

A. New York Giants

B. Washington Redskins

C. Dallas Cowboys

D. Tampa Bay Buccaneers

64. After leaving the Ravens, Jamal Lewis played for which divisional rival?

A. Buffalo Bills

B. Cleveland Browns

C. New England Patriots

D. Pittsburgh Steelers

65. Terrell Suggs set a Ravens team record in what category?

A. Rushing Yards

B. Interceptions

C. Sacks

D. Passes Deflected

66. How many yards did Priest Holmes rush for in 2000, his last in Baltimore before leaving for the Chiefs?

    A. 1,241

    B. 1,008

    C. 588

    D. 875

67. In the Ravens' first five years (1996-2000), how many different season leaders did the team have in receiving?

    A. 5

    B. 4

    C. 1

    D. 2

68. The Ravens' 2012 season was dedicated to what former owner?

    A. Art Modell

    B. Pete Rozelle

    C. Al Davis

    D. George Halas

69. Ray Rice was the only player to rush for 100 yards against which divisional rival in 2009?

A. Oakland Raiders

B. Cleveland Browns

C. Miami Dolphins

D. Pittsburgh Steelers

70. A Jamal Lewis fumble in overtime led to a Baltimore Ravens loss against which team in 2003?

A. St. Louis Rams

B. Cincinnati Bengals

C. Seattle Seahawks

D. Miami Dolphins

71. Which team handed Baltimore Ravens coach Brian Billick his first defeat as an NFL head coach?

A. St. Louis Rams

B. Minnesota Vikings

C. New Orleans Saints

D. Chicago Bears

72. Which team did the Baltimore Ravens defeat with the first shutout in franchise history?

    A. Cincinnati Bengals

    B. Houston Oilers

    C. Cleveland Browns

    D. Buffalo Bills

73. What was the name of the HBO special filmed during the 2001 Baltimore Ravens training camp?

    A. Hard Knocks

    B. Champion Training

    C. Pigskin Camp

    D. Champ Camp

74. In 1998, the Baltimore Ravens returned two kickoffs for 90+ yards against which team?

    A. Miami Dolphins

    B. Denver Broncos

    C. Minnesota Vikings

    D. Cincinnati Bengal

75. In 2007, how much did a lower-level midfield ticket to a Baltimore Ravens home game cost?

    A. 100

    B. 115

    C. 150

    D. 85

76. Which Baltimore Ravens player was the first to surpass 8,000 combined yards?

    A. Jamal Lewis

    B. Travis Taylor

    C. B.J. Sams

    D. Jermaine Lewis

77. Which Baltimore Ravens player was inducted into the Ravens' "Ring of Honor" in 2004?

    A. Peter Boulware

    B. Michael McCrary

    C. Ray Lewis

    D. Earnest Byner

78. Who led the Baltimore Ravens in passing yards during the 1998 NFL season?

A. Eric Zeier

B. Vinny Testaverde

C. Jim Harbaugh

D. Tony Banks

79. The Baltimore Ravens led the NFL in what defensive category in 2005?

A. Yards Allowed Per Game

B. Opp. Net Punting Avg.

C. First Downs Allowed

D. Opponent Rushing Avg.

80. In 2001, who ended the Baltimore Ravens' streak of 50 games without allowing a 100-yard rush?

A. Ahman Green

B. Corey Dillon

C. LaDainian Tomlinson

D. Priest Holmes

81. In 2005, how many games in a row did the Baltimore Ravens win?

    A. Two

    B. Four

    C. Six

    D. Eight

82. In 2005 how many yards receiving did Randy Hymes average per game?

    A. 4

    B. 45

    C. 12

    D. 34

83. What team did linebacker Bart Scott turn down when he re-signed with the Baltimore Ravens in 2005?

    A. Green Bay Packers

    B. Cleveland Browns

    C. Jacksonville Jaguars

    D. New England Patriots

84. Prior to the 2006 season, what was the only AFC team the Ravens had never beaten?

    A. Denver Broncos

    B. Buffalo Bills

    C. New England Patriots

    D. Kansas City Chiefs

85. Who did the Ravens select with their first-ever draft pick, in 1996?

    A. Jermaine Lewis

    B. Jonathan Ogden

    C. Peter Boulware

    D. Ray Lewis

86. Tony Banks and who else served as back-ups to Trent Dilfer in the 2000 season?

    A. Randall Cunningham

    B. Chris Redman

    C. Elvis Grbac

    D. Scott Mitchel

87. Which of these former Ravens players was actually an undrafted free agent out of college?

    A. Jamal Lewis

    B. Brandon Stokley

    C. Priest Holmes

    D. Chris Redman

88. Against which team did Baltimore Raven Jamal Lewis put up 500 yards rushing in 2003?

    A. Cleveland Browns

    B. Pittsburgh Steelers

    C. Jacksonville Jaguars

    D. Cincinnati Bengals

89. In 2003 Jamal Lewis was how many yards shy of Eric Dickerson's single-season rushing record?

    A. 39

    B. 52

    C. 6

    D. 12

90. In the 2003 wild-card loss to Tennessee, which Raven player was called for unsportsmanlike conduct late in the game?

   A. Orlando Brown

   B. Ray Lewis

   C. Todd Heap

   D. Will Demps

91. Who was the first Baltimore Ravens quarterback to throw for 400 yards in a single game?

   A. Tony Banks

   B. Vinny Testaverde

   C. Steve McNair

   D. Eric Zeier

92. Who led the 2006 Baltimore Ravens with 13 sacks?

   A. Trevor Pryce

   B. Terrell Suggs

   C. Bart Scott

   D. Adalius Thomas

93. Who led the 2006 Baltimore Ravens with 73 receptions?

   A. Derrick Mason

   B. Mark Clayton

   C. Todd Heap

   D. Demetrius Williams

94. Who was the first Baltimore Raven to amass 200 or more receiving yards in a single game?

   A. Derrick Alexander

   B. Floyd Turner

   C. Qadry Ismail

   D. Michael Jackson

95. Who was the only player to represent the Baltimore Ravens in the 2005 Pro Bowl?

   A. Chris McAlister

   B. Ray Lewis

   C. Jonathan Ogden

   D. Ed Reed

B. Facts

I. Greatest Ravens of all time

1. Derrick Mason

1. Derrick James Mason (born January 17, 1974) is a former American football wide receiver who played

for   fifteen   seasons   in   the National   Football League (NFL).

2. He was drafted by the Tennessee Oilers in the fourth round   of   the 1997   NFL   Draft after   playing college football for   the Michigan   State   Spartans. Following eight seasons with the Oilers and Titans, including two Pro   Bowl selections   (2000 and 2003),   Mason signed with the Baltimore Ravens in 2005.

3. He became the Ravens' all-time leading receiver with 5,777 yards from 2005 to 2010, but he was released before the 2011 season. He spent 2011 with the New York Jets and Houston Texans. Mason retired as a Baltimore Raven on June 11, 2012. He was the last active NFL player to have played for the Oilers.

4. Mason   played college   football at Michigan   State. During his four-year career, he set a team record for kick-off return yards of 2,384. He also caught eight touchdowns.

5. He played under Nick Saban in 1995 and 1996 where he would catch 106 passes for 1,652 yards and 6 TD. He also played alongside Muhsin Muhammad in 1995.

6. Mason signed with the Baltimore Ravens as a free agent on March 7, 2005. In his first year with the team,

he started in all 16 games and recorded 86 receptions, a Ravens franchise season record.

7. In 2006, he played in 16 games with 15 starts and finished the campaign with 68 receptions for 750 yards and two touchdowns. Mason caught the pass that gave Steve McNair 30,000 passing yards for his career in the 19-7 win in the season finale against the Buffalo Bills. The following year, Mason had 103 receptions for 1,087 yards and five touchdowns. Mason became the first player in Ravens history to record 100 receptions in a season. He also had a 79-yard score.

8. In 2008, Mason was selected as a third alternate wide receiver for the Pro Bowl. In 2008, he had 80 receptions for 1037 receiving yards and 5 touchdowns. He was the primary target for rookie quarterback Joe Flacco. Mason dislocated his shoulder when he fell after a catch in a game against the Houston Texans, eventually coming back to finish the contest. Mason also played

with a shoulder he separated against the New York Giants.

9. Mason re-aggravated of his injury against the Dallas Cowboys, but finished the game with six catches for 66 yards and one touchdown. He led the team with a postseason career-high 12 receptions for 190 yards, including a postseason career long 48-yard touchdown reception.

10. The 2009 season saw Mason continue his solid production with 73 catches for 1,028 yards. Mason scored seven times, two more than the previous year.

11. On November 21, 2010, Mason caught his 900th reception, becoming the 13th receiver in NFL history to do so. In a 2010 game against the Carolina Panthers, Mason and Flacco got into an argument on the sidelines. Mason was reportedly upset that Flacco was late in getting a pass to him. The two apparently settled their differences. Mason had 61 catches for 802 yards and seven scores that season.

12. When the NFL announced the new collective bargaining agreement on July 25, 2011, the Ravens announced their intention to release Mason upon the start of free agency to free salary cap space. He was formally released by the team on July 28.

2.   Lamar Jackson

1. Jackson was born in Pompano Beach, Florida, on January 7, 1997. He attended Boynton Beach High School in Boynton Beach, Florida.[1] He was rated by Rivals.com as a four-star recruit and committed to the University of Louisville to play college football.

2. On January 5, 2018, Jackson officially announced that he would be entering the 2018 NFL Draft. Controversy arose when draft pundits doubted Jackson's quarterback abilities and suggested that he switch positions due to his athleticism, but he remained adamant in playing quarterback professionally. As a result, he declined to run drills such as the 40-yard dash during the NFL Scouting Combine to focus on displaying his passing skills.

3. Jackson was drafted by the Baltimore Ravens in the first round with the 32nd overall pick in the draft, who traded up for the selection with the Philadelphia Eagles. He was the fifth quarterback selected that year.

4. Jackson made his first regular-season appearance relieving starting quarterback Joe Flacco in the second half of a 47-3 victory against the Buffalo Bills, finishing with 24 passing yards and 39 rushing yards.

5. During Week 7, Jackson scored his first NFL touchdown on a 1-yard run as the Ravens narrowly lost to the New Orleans Saints by a score of 24–23. Jackson threw his first NFL touchdown pass, a 26-yard completion to fellow rookie tight end Hayden Hurst, the next week in relief of Flacco in the fourth quarter of a 36–21 loss to the Carolina Panthers.

6. On November 18, 2018, Jackson made his first start against the Cincinnati Bengals in place of the injured Joe Flacco, who injured his hip two weeks prior against the Pittsburgh Steelers. Jackson went 13 for 19 for 150 yards and an interception and rushed for 117 yards, which was a Ravens franchise record for rushing yards by a quarterback in a single game in a 24–21 victory. The following week against the Oakland

Raiders, Jackson threw for 178 yards, one touchdown, and two interceptions. He also rushed for 71 yards and a rushing touchdown. The Ravens won by a score of 34–17. During Week 13 against the Atlanta Falcons, Jackson passed for 125 yards and rushed for 75 yards and a touchdown in a 26–16 victory. In a Week 14 27–24 overtime loss to the Kansas City Chiefs, Jackson threw two touchdowns for the first time in his career.

7. Jackson helped the Ravens defeat the Los Angeles Chargers in Week 16, completing 12 of 22 passes for a career-high 204 yards and a touchdown in a 22–10 upset victory. The following week against fellow rookie quarterback Baker Mayfield and the Cleveland Browns, Jackson passed for 179 yards and rushed for two touchdowns on 95 rushing yards, despite fumbling a third potential touchdown at the goal line, as the Ravens beat the Browns 26–24 to clinch the AFC North title. In the seven regular season games in which Jackson had started, the Ravens went 6–1 to close out the 2018 season. Overall, he finished with 1,201 passing yards, six passing touchdowns, and three interceptions. In addition, he led all quarterbacks with 695 rushing yards and added five rushing touchdowns.

8. The Ravens faced off at home against the Chargers in a rematch during the Wild Card Round of the playoffs. Despite being held to just 25 passing yards at one point in the fourth quarter by a stout Chargers defense,

Jackson then passed for two touchdowns in four minutes to bring the Ravens back from a 20-point deficit to within a touchdown. After forcing the Chargers to punt with less than a minute left, the Ravens had one last chance to win the game down six points, but Jackson was strip-sacked by Chargers linebacker Uchenna Nwosu. With the Chargers recovering the ball, the Ravens lost 23–17 and were knocked out of the playoffs. Jackson finished the game completing 14 of 29 passes for 194 yards, the two aforementioned touchdowns, and an interception while rushing for 54 yards, losing one fumble.

3. Todd Heap

1. Todd Benjamin Heap (born March 16, 1980 in Mesa, Arizona) is a Pro Bowl tight end for the Baltimore Ravens of the National Football League. He played college football at Arizona State University.

2. At Mountain View High School, in Mesa, Arizona, he was Mountain 5A Player of the Year. In the state championship game, he threw a 26-yard touchdown pass.

3. Heap played college football at Arizona State University, majoring in pre-business. His 115 receptions broke the school record for tight ends, previously held by Ken Dyer.

4. The Baltimore Ravens selected Heap with the 31st overall pick in the 2001 NFL Draft. Through the end of

the 2009 NFL season he has played 120 total career games, starting 115.

5. Heap recorded 16 receptions for 206 yards and one touchdown in his rookie season, playing behind eight-time Pro-Bowler Shannon Sharpe.

6. Heap became the starting tight end for the Ravens in 2002 after Sharpe left in free agency. The Ravens were 7-9 in Heap's second season. He caught 68 passes for 836 yards and 6 touchdowns and was voted to his first Pro Bowl.

7. The following season in 2003, Heap garnered 57 receptions for 693 yards and 3 touchdowns, despite the Ravens having a run-first offense, behind the record breaking 2066 yard rushing season of Jamal Lewis. Heap was again voted to the Pro Bowl as the Ravens won the AFC North division for the first time. Heap had 6 receptions for 80 yards and a touchdown in a 20-17 playoff loss to the Tennessee Titans.

8. Heap was injured in the second week of the 2004 season, in a game against the Pittsburgh Steelers. He returned in week 13, but missed the final game of the season. He finished the season with 303 yards and 3 touchdowns in six games.

9. Heap returned healthy and ready to play in the 2005 season. The Ravens team suffered numerous injuries to their starters and ended the season 6-10. Heap caught 75 passes for 855 yards and 7 touchdowns.

10. 2006 would see Todd Heap receiving passes from former rival, former Pro Bowl QB Steve McNair. 2006 would also prove to be the Ravens best regular season, as they won the AFC North for the second time in franchise history with a record of 13-3. Heap caught 73 passes for 765 yards and 6 touchdowns.

11. Heap missed 10 games in the 2007 season due to injury, and caught only 23 passes, amassing 239 yards and one touchdown.

12. Heap collected 35 receptions for 403 yards and 3 touchdowns. The Ravens advanced to the AFC Championship Game for the first time since the 2000 season, but would lose to the Steelers.

13. Heap played through numerous injuries in the 2009 season, yet had 53 receptions for 593 yards and 6 touchdowns, and twice scored two touchdowns in a single game. The Ravens finished 9-7, losing in the second round of the playoffs to the Indianapolis Colts.

14. Heap is a devout member of The Church of Jesus Christ of Latter-day Saints. He and his wife, Ashley, have a daughter, Brooklyn (born 2002) and twin boys, Preston and Kyle, (born 2006). He is one of six children. His mother's cousin is Arizona State Hall of Fame QB and former Dallas Cowboys QB Danny White and his great uncle, Verl, played basketball at Arizona State.

4. Haloti Ngata

1. Etuini Haloti Ngata (IPA: [ˈŋata]; born January 21, 1984) is a former American football defensive tackle. He played college football for the University of Oregon and earned consensus All-American honors.

2. Ngata was drafted by the Baltimore Ravens in the first round of the 2006 NFL Draft, and was selected for the Pro Bowl five times. Ngata decided to leave Oregon a year early because his mother, 'Ofa, was in the early stages of kidney dialysis. She died from her illness on January 13, 2006.

3. Ngata was selected by the Baltimore Ravens in the first round with the 12th overall pick in the 2006 NFL Draft. It was the first time in franchise history the Ravens used a first round pick on a defensive lineman. Ngata became the highest selected defensive lineman from the current Pac-12 conference since Andre Carter in 2001.

4. On July 28, 2006, Ngata ended a brief contract holdout by agreeing to a 5-year contract worth up to $14 million with the Baltimore Ravens. In his rookie season, he started in all 16 games and finished the campaign with 31 tackles, one sack, and an interception. The following season, he made 63 tackles and three sacks. Ngata had two interceptions in 2008.

5. In the 2008 season, Ngata started all 16 regular season and three postseason games. He led the Ravens defensive line with 77 total tackles (43 Solo, 34 Assist), one sack, a career-high 2 Interceptions, and 5 passes deflected as part of the NFL's #2 passing defense. He was named to the Pro Bowl as a first alternate and earned Second-Team All-Pro honors by the Associated Press for the first time in his career.

6. During the 2009 season, Ngata started all 16 Ravens regular season and both post-season games. During the regular season, he recorded 36 tackles, of which 26

were unassisted and 1.5 sacks. He was selected for the first time in his career to play in the NFL Pro Bowl.

7. After an outstanding 2010 season which included 63 tackles and 5.5 sacks, Ngata was selected to the 2010 All-Fundamentals Team by USA Football and the NFL Players Association.

8. On February 15, the Ravens placed their franchise tag on Ngata. On September 20, he was signed to a 5-year deal worth $61 million.

9. The Ravens opened the 2011 season at home against the Pittsburgh Steelers on September 11. In the game Ngata forced a fumble and tipped a pass that led to a Ray Lewis interception; the Ravens won 35-7. Two weeks later against the St. Louis Rams, Ray Lewis sacked Sam Bradford. Bradford fumbled, and the ball was recovered by Ngata who scored his first career regular season touchdown.

10. On October 2, 2011, during the Ravens game against the New York Jets, Ngata sacked Jets quarterback Mark

Sanchez, causing Sanchez to fumble the ball. Ravens linebacker Jarrett Johnson picked up the fumble and returned it for a touchdown. The Ravens won the game by a score of 34-17. After reviewing the hit, the NFL levied a $15,000 fine against Ngata for roughing the passer even though no penalty was called by officials during the game.

11. Ngata finished the season with a career-high 64 tackles (36 unassisted), along with 5 sacks, 2 forced fumbles, and 5 passes defended. Ngata also earned his third straight Pro Bowl appearance.

12. During the 2012 season, Ngata played mostly defensive tackle and sometimes defensive end, collecting 5 sacks and 51 tackles overall. Ngata played in all four games of the Ravens 2012 postseason, recording 10 solo tackles and 3 assisted tackles as he helped the Ravens to victory in Super Bowl XLVII.

13. In 2013, Ngata played mostly as a nose tackle making 33 tackles, 1.5 sacks, and 3 passes defended in 15 games played.

14. On December 4, 2014, Ngata was suspended for four games after he violated the NFL's policy on performance-enhancing substances.

5. Marshall Yanda

1. Marshal John Yanda (born September 15, 1984) is a former American football guard. He played college football at the University of Iowa, and was drafted by the Baltimore Ravens in the third round of the 2007

NFL Draft and spent his entire 13-year career with the team.

2. With six consecutive Pro Bowl selections from 2011 to 2016 (the longest active streak amongst guards at the time) Yanda was widely considered to be among the best offensive linemen in football; he was also a unanimous selection to the NFL 2010s All-Decade Team. Yanda missed most of the 2017 season due to injury, but was elected to the Pro Bowl again in 2018

and 2019 before announcing his retirement in March 2020.

3. Yanda attended Anamosa High School in Iowa and was a letterman in football, basketball, and track & field. In football, he was a two-time first team all-conference selection.

4. Yanda played for the Iowa Hawkeyes football team while attending the University of Iowa, where he was an economics major. He was selected as a third-team All-American by The NFL Draft Report in 2006 and earned second-team All-Big Ten honors from the league's coaches in recognition of his contributions on the field. Yanda's first two college football seasons were played for North Iowa Area Community College.

5. The Baltimore Ravens selected Yanda in the third round (86th overall) of the 2007 NFL Draft. Yanda was the seventh offensive tackle drafted in 2007.

6. On July 11, 2007, the Baltimore Ravens signed Yanda to a three-year, $1.61 million contract that includes $502,698 guaranteed.

7. During his rookie year in 2007, Yanda played all 16 games with 12 stars. In 2008, Yanda was limited to five starts. In 2009, Yanda played all 16 games with nine starts. In 2010, Yanda started all 16 games for the first time of his career. On July 26, 2011, the Ravens re-signed Yanda to a five-year, $32 million contract. In 2011, Yanda again started all 16 games and was chosen to represent the AFC in the 2011 Pro Bowl. In 2012, Yanda started 14 games and won his first championship ring as the Ravens won Super Bowl XLVII against the San Francisco 49ers. In the 2013 and 2014 seasons, Yanda played all 16 games each season.

8. On October 16, 2015, the Ravens signed Yanda to a four-year contract extension worth $32 million.

9. Yanda was consecutively named as the top-ranked guard by Pro Football Focus in 2014, 2015, and 2016.

He was ranked 37th by his fellow players on the NFL Top 100 Players of 2016.

10. Yanda was named to his sixth straight Pro Bowl in recognition of his accomplishments in the 2016 season.

He was also ranked 43rd by his peers on the NFL Top 100 Players of 2017.

11. Yanda broke his ankle during a game on September 17, 2017, which prematurely ended his season.

12. On December 18, 2018, Yanda was named to his seventh Pro Bowl after missing out last year, due to his injury. He was also named second-team All-Pro for the fourth time in his career after starting all 16 games.

13. On April 11, 2019, Yanda signed a one-year contract extension with the Ravens through the 2020 season.

14. On March 10, 2020, Yanda announced his retirement from the NFL after 13 seasons.

15. Yanda married Shannon Hunt Yanda in 2011. The couple have three children: Graham, Libby, and Logan. They spend the NFL off-season in Marion, Iowa.

6. Terrell Suggs

1. Suggs was drafted by the Baltimore Ravens 10th overall in the 2003 NFL Draft, becoming one of the

youngest defensive players ever drafted at only 20 years old until defensive tackle Amobi Okoye was drafted by the Houston Texans at the age of 19 in 2007.

2. Suggs enjoyed immediate success as a rookie in 2003 as he tied an NFL record by posting a sack in each of his first four games. He finished the season with 27 tackles (19 solo), 12 sacks (a Ravens franchise rookie record, 6 forced fumbles, 2 pass deflections and 1 interception, earning him Defensive Rookie of the Year honors while only starting one game that year.

3. The next season in 2004, he was elected to his first Pro Bowl as he recorded 10.5 sacks and 60 tackles (45 solo).

4. In 2005, the Ravens' new defensive co-ordinator Rex Ryan, son of famous defensive coordinator Buddy Ryan, moved Suggs from outside linebacker to defensive end in many of the defensive schemes. Despite registering a then-career-low 8 sacks, Suggs also set new career-highs in tackles with 69 (46 solo) and interceptions with 2.

5. In 2006, Suggs was part of the NFL's best overall defense, the unit allowing a league-low 12.6 points per game. He recorded 64 tackles (46 solo), 9.5 sacks and

set new career-high in pass deflections with 8. After the season, he was voted to the Pro Bowl for the second time. He was a major contributor as the Ravens went 13-3. For the season, Suggs started nine games at right defensive end in the Ravens base 4-3 and seven games at outside linebacker when the Ravens started the game in a base 3-4 defense. Suggs also earned attention for his flashy playing style, "Suggs evolved into one of the league's best pass-rushers whether he is blitzing as a linebacker or rushing from defensive end with one hand on the ground."

6. The following season in 2007, Suggs made 80 tackles (52 solo) and five sacks, as he and the Ravens plummeted to 5-11. Like the season before, Suggs was a hybrid defensive end/linebacker, playing 50 percent of the defensive snaps at defensive end in the Ravens base 4-3 defense.

7. On February 19, 2008, the Ravens placed the franchise tag on Suggs. He initially filed a grievance because the

team had designated him as a LB with the franchise tag rather than a DE, which resulted in a monetary difference of about $800,000. Despite being unhappy with the franchise tag, Suggs reported to off-season mini-camps to practice with the team. On May 13, 2008, he reached an agreement with the team to split the difference in the franchise tag amounts of a LB and a DE and drop his grievance.

8. In Week 7 of the 2008 NFL season, Suggs intercepted a pass from Chad Pennington of the Miami Dolphins and returned it 44 yards for a touchdown, the first pick of his professional career. Two weeks later, he intercepted Derek Anderson of the Cleveland Browns for a game-sealing touchdown. At season's end, he was named to his third Pro Bowl after producing 68 tackles (53 solo), 2 forced fumbles and 8 sacks to go along with the 2 interceptions, a new career-high 9 pass break-ups and 2 touchdowns. During the 2008–09 NFL playoffs, Suggs recorded sacks in all three of the

Ravens' post-season games, including two in the AFC Championship game against Ben Roethlisberger, whom Suggs sacked often over the years.

9. On February 18, 2009, he was once again given the Ravens' franchise tag. On July 15, 2009 the Ravens signed him to a 6-year, $62.5 million contract. His bonus money ($33.1 million) made him the highest paid linebacker in NFL history.

10. The 2009 season was not as productive for Suggs as he recorded a career-low in sacks with 4.5. Playing above

his normal playing weight, he also missed the first three games of his career due to injury after quarterback Brady Quinn dove at his legs after cornerback Chris Carr intercepted a pass. In the wild Card playoff game against the New England Patriots, Suggs sacked and forced a Tom Brady fumble before recovering the ball on the Patriots' opening drive, helping the Ravens ultimately win 33–14.

7. Jonathan Ogden

1. Jonathan Phillip Ogden (born July 31, 1974) is a former American football offensive tackle who played his entire career with the Baltimore Ravens of the National Football League (NFL). He played college football for the University of California, Los Angeles (UCLA), and was recognized as a unanimous All-American. He was drafted by the Ravens 4th overall in the 1996 NFL Draft. He was an eleven-time Pro Bowl selection and a nine-time All-Pro.

2. On February 2, 2013, Ogden was voted into the Pro Football Hall of Fame, the first inductee to spend his entire playing career as a Raven. He was inducted into the College Football Hall of Fame in 2012.

3. Ogden decided to attend the University of California, Los Angeles (UCLA) instead of the University of Florida because the UCLA Bruins football coaches would let him participate in track and field. As a sophomore, he helped UCLA to the 1993 Pac-10

Championship and Rose Bowl. He later won the 1996 NCAA Men's Division I Indoor Track and Field Championships in the shot put, with a personal best of 19.42 meters. Ogden had an outstanding career with the Bruins football team, starting as left tackle for four years. In 23 games during his junior and senior years, he allowed just two sacks. In 1995, Ogden received the Outland Trophy and the Morris Trophy, was the UPI Lineman of the Year, and was a unanimous first-team All-American. Ogden's father, an investment banker, told his son to accept UCLA's decision to move him from right to left tackle.

4. Ogden's jersey was retired, making him only the eighth player in UCLA history to receive that honor. He was inducted into the UCLA Athletics Hall of Fame in 2006. On December 5, was enshrined into the College Football Hall of Fame.

5. During the 1996 NFL Draft, Ogden was selected by the Baltimore Ravens in the first round with the fourth

overall choice, the first-ever draft pick made by the Ravens. Ozzie Newsome wanted to select Ogden but owner, Art Modell wanted to select Lawrence Phillips. Phillips played in 3 NFL seasons and rushed for a career yardage total of 1,453.

6. He was named a four-time All-Pro And an eleven-time Pro Bowler at left tackle, earning trips to Hawaii in every season except his rookie year. During his career, Ogden caught two passes – both for one yard and both for touchdowns. He also recovered 10 fumbles, and recorded 10 tackles. Ogden also won a reputation for smiling. "He's a laugher," joked former New York Giants DE Michael Strahan. "You see him, you think to yourself this guy is not mean enough to handle the mean guys out there in the NFL. Jonathan would rip your limbs off, and he'd smile...and wave your arm in front of you." Ogden also threw his helmet in frustration several times. He is widely considered one of the best tackles to ever play the game.

7. In 2001, Ogden won a Super Bowl ring with the Ravens when they defeated the New York Giants 34–7 in Super Bowl XXXV. Ogden announced his retirement on June 12, 2008 after a career that spanned 12 seasons, all with Baltimore. His retirement left Ray Lewis and Matt Stover as the last remaining Ravens from the team's inaugural season in Baltimore. At 6' 9", Ogden was tied with fellow Raven Jared Gaither and Bengals tackle Dennis Roland as the tallest player in the NFL at the end of his playing career.

8. Ogden served as the Ravens' honorary captain at Super Bowl XLVII, which saw his former team win their second world championship.

9. Ogden married Kema Hunt in 2004. The couple reside in Las Vegas. He established the Jonathan Ogden Foundation to benefit inner city schools and help student-athletes take responsibility for their futures through lessons learned on the playing field, in the classroom, and throughout their local communities.

10. On May 1, 2000, Ogden appeared on WWE Raw along with members of the Baltimore Ravens and attempted to win the WWF Hardcore Championship from Crash Holly after Holly was attacked by Steve Blackman, but was unsuccessful. In September 2009, Ogden was selected to Sporting News' Magazine's Team of the Decade (2000's). In 2010, he was placed 72nd on the list of NFL's top 100 players. He was present during the Ravens' Super Bowl XXXV reunion in 2010.

11. Ogden has starred in commercials for Apple Ford, a dealership in Columbia, Maryland, and during his

playing career he appeared in TV advertisements for GEBCO, a local car insurance company. He also appeared in a 2012 advertisement with Baltimore Mayor Stephanie Rawlings-Blake in support of Maryland Question 7. The measure expanded gambling in the state.

8. Ed Reed

1. After his college career, Reed was drafted by the Baltimore Ravens in the first round (24th overall pick) of the 2002 NFL Draft.

2. In his rookie season, Reed started in all 16 games and finished the campaign with 85 tackles, one sack and five interceptions. The following year he finished the season with 71 tackles and seven interceptions and was voted to his first Pro Bowl.

3. In 2004, Reed was named the NFL Defensive Player of the Year by the Associated Press. In addition to his record return in 2004, Reed set an NFL mark for most

interception return yardage in a season, accumulating 358 return yards on 9 interceptions; Reed held this record until 2009, when it was exceeded by Darren Sharper. He also returned an interception 106 yards for a touchdown, which was an NFL record until Reed himself broke it in 2008. Also in 2004, Reed became the only player in Pro Bowl history to block a punt and return it for a touchdown. In 2005, Reed only played in ten games due to an ankle injury and finished the campaign with 37 tackles and one interception.

4. In 2006, Reed recorded 60 tackles and 5 interceptions and was voted to his third Pro Bowl. In 2007, he made 39 tackles and 7 interceptions. In the 2008 Pro Bowl he recorded two interceptions, tying the Pro Bowl record.

5. During a game against the Philadelphia Eagles on November 23, 2008, Reed returned an interception for what was originally reported as an 108-yard touchdown return (later officially adjusted to 107 yards by the Elias Sports Bureau). This set an NFL record,

breaking his own record of 106 yards set in 2004 against the Cleveland Browns. The ball he intercepted and the jersey he wore during the play are now in the Hall of Fame. In the Ravens' 2008 AFC Wild Card game against the Miami Dolphins, Reed intercepted Chad Pennington twice, returning one for a touchdown.

6. He intercepted three passes in 2009, returning one for a 50-yard touchdown against the Cincinnati Bengals, and added two more interceptions in the playoffs, but fumbled one away in a 20-3 loss to the Indianapolis Colts.

7. Reed was the only player unanimously voted onto the AP 2008 NFL All-Pro team. In 2009, Reed was selected to the Sporting News's Team of the Decade (2000's).

8. In 2010, Reed led the NFL in interceptions with 8, despite only playing in 10 games due to hip surgery.

9. Reed also intercepted T. J. Yates in the fourth quarter of the 2011 AFC Divisional Round. After deflecting another pass later to seal the win, Reed was injured slightly, but played the next week in an AFC Championship loss to the New England Patriots.

10. Reed skipped out on a mandatory minicamp, but showed up for training camp. In Week 1 of the 2012 season, Reed returned an Andy Dalton interception 34

yards for a touchdown against the Cincinnati Bengals, making Reed the NFL's all-time leader in interception return yards. On November 19, Reed was given a 1 game suspension by the league "for repeated violations of the rule prohibiting hits to the head and neck area of defenseless players" following an unnecessary roughness call for a hit on Emmanuel Sanders. Reed was considered a repeat offender based on his prior hits to Deion Branch earlier in the season and to Drew Brees in 2010. This suspension was later overturned, and Reed was fined $50,000 for the hit.

11. Reed said on January 24, 2013 that despite repeated reports he might retire, he intends to play next year. Reed finally earned his first Super Bowl ring when the Ravens defeated the San Francisco 49ers 34-31 in Super Bowl XLVII. In that game, Reed intercepted Colin Kaepernick for his ninth career postseason interception, which tied the NFL record. This interception was the 49ers' first interception, and

the final score resulted in the 49ers' first Super Bowl loss in their franchise's history.

12. Reed became a free agent after his contract expired at the end of the 2012 season. While he had considered retiring after the 2012 season, Reed stated after the Super Bowl that he intends to continue playing football in 2013.

13. Reed has scored a total of 13 touchdowns in his career with the Baltimore Ravens — 3 blocked punts, 1 punt return, 2 fumble returns and 7 interception returns.

9. Ray Lewis

1. Lewis was the top rated inside linebacker heading into the 1996 NFL Draft, but Kevin Hardy was considered the draft's only outstanding prospect at linebacker. The fifth linebacker selected in the draft, scouts saw Lewis' strengths as his speed, tackling and intensity, but many considered his lack of size a potential liability. Lewis earned USA Today's All-Rookie team honors after leading the Ravens in tackles (110) in the 1996 season. His 15 tackles for loss led the NFL. He added 2.5 sacks, 6 pass deflections, and an interception on the season.

2. Lewis recorded an NFL best 184 tackles in 1997, earning his first Pro Bowl berth at the end of that season. In addition, Lewis totaled 4 sacks, an interception, a forced fumble, a fumble recovery, and 11 pass deflections.

3. In 1998, Lewis made his second trip to the Pro Bowl after recording 120 tackles, 3 sacks, 2 interceptions, a forced fumble, and 7 pass deflections leading the Ravens in tackles for the third consecutive season. He

was also named to The Sporting News All-Pro Team. In what would prove to be Hall of Fame running back Barry Sanders' final game, Lewis and the rest of the Ravens defense held him to just 41 rushing yards.

4. In 1999, Lewis led the NFL in tackles with 168. He was named to a third straight Pro Bowl and was named to the All-Pro 1st team. He also totaled 3.5 sacks, 3 interceptions, 8 pass deflections, a safety, and a forced fumble. Lewis also won the 1999 NFL Alumni Linebacker Of The Year chosen by past NFL ALUMNI professional players, who chose according to the position in which they played.

5. In 2000, Lewis led a defense which set a 16-game single season record for fewest points allowed (165) and fewest rushing yards allowed (970). The team recorded four shutouts, one shy of the single season record. The unit finished 1st league-wide in six key defensive categories. Lewis won Super Bowl XXXV MVP honors, Defensive Player of the Year honors, earned a

unanimous All-Pro selection, and was once again named to start in the Pro Bowl. Lewis' regular season total of 137 tackles once again led the Ravens, and Lewis added 31 tackles, two interceptions, nine pass deflections, one fumble recovery and a touchdown in the four game playoff run.

6. In 2001, Lewis earned his 5th consecutive Pro Bowl selection when he led the NFL in tackles 162 and earned 1st-team All-Pro honors. Lewis scored a touchdown in the 2002 Pro Bowl. In the Raven's 2 playoff games Lewis totaled 17 tackles, 3 forced fumbles, and 1 pass deflection.

7. In 2002, Lewis was limited to five games due to a shoulder injury. He still managed to rank 5th on the team with 58 tackles. In addition, Lewis earned two interceptions, two pass deflections, a forced fumble and a fumble recovery. Lewis earned AFC Defensive Player of the Week honors in Week 4 vs. the Denver Broncos after posting 18 tackles (11 solo), two pass

deflections and an interception on "Monday Night Football". After having been selected to the Pro Bowl for five consecutive seasons (1997–2001), Lewis's streak was stopped by his season ending injury. In his absence, the Baltimore Ravens defense would finish ranked 19th in points allowed.

8. Lewis was the leading vote recipient for the 2003 AP All-Pro team, earning 49 of 50 votes. He also won the annual AP NFL Defensive Player of the Year with 43 votes out of 50. Additionally, Lewis earned Pro Football Weekly, PFWA and Football Digest Defensive MVP honors and was named to Dr. Z's Sports Illustrated All-Pro team, Pro Football Weekly's All-NFL team, Pro Football Weekly's All-AFC team, Football Digest's All-Pro 1st-team, and The Sporting News' All-Pro team. Lewis also earned the KC 101 AFC Defensive Player of the Year award for the 3rd time in four years, the 2003 NFL Alumni Linebacker Of The Year, and finished with 161 tackles, 1.5 sacks, 6 interceptions, 2 forced

fumbles, 2 fumble recoveries, 14 pass deflections, and 1 touchdown. He was named NFL Defensive Player of the Month for November and AFC Defensive Player of the week for his fifteen-tackle, one-interception performance against the Pittsburgh Steelers in Week 17. In the playoffs Lewis totaled 17 tackles.

9. In 2004, Lewis was named 1st-team All Pro by the AP, 2nd-team "All Pro" by College and Pro Football Weekly and Football Digest, and "All Pro" by The Sporting News. He finished the season with 146 total

tackles, 1 sack, 2 fumble recoveries, 1 fumble forced, and 6 pass deflections.

10. Lewis' 2005 season was cut short by a week 6 injury. He was placed on injury reserve in week 8, having amassed 46 tackles, a sack, an interception, 2 pass deflections, and a fumble recovery in the season's first 6 games.

11. In 2006, Lewis led the Ravens defense to an NFL best ranking in 14 major defensive categories, including total yards allowed, points per game allowed, and interceptions. The Ravens also finished second in sacks, take-aways, and rushing yards allowed. Lewis missed two games due to injury but still recorded 103 tackles, a personal best five sacks, two interceptions, and eight pass deflections in 14 Games. He also forced a fumble and recovered one. The Ravens allowed just one 100-yard rushing performance in the 14 games Lewis played. Lewis was named AFC Defensive Player of the week following his 7 tackle, one sack, and three pass

deflection performance against the Tampa Bay Buccaneers in Week 1. He was also selected to the Pro Bowl but withdrew because of a hand injury, ceding his spot to fellow Ravens Linebacker Bart Scott. Lewis finished fifth in Defensive Player of the Year voting. Lewis totaled 15 tackles and a pass deflection in the playoffs.

II. Fun facts

1. Pretty much like any other team in the world, for any sport, the Baltimore Ravens have a following that is in a class of its own. Whether it is the shirtless guy who did the worm at the Bank recently or the football enthusiasts who get the NFL Game Pass app with a VPN that allows them never to miss a game no matter where they are, there is a sense of passion and euphoria attached with the Ravens that is heart-

warming. This makes them one of the most cherished and respected teams in the entire NFL.

2. There is a certain nostalgic charm in knowing that the Baltimore Ravens are one of only two NFL teams that have a marching band. They are also the largest band in the NFL based on the total number of members. Known as the Baltimore Marching Ravens, they have been performing now for the last 70 years, earlier with the Colts and then the Ravens. The Marching Ravens have also been the focus of a documentary "The Band

That Wouldn't Die" which was directed by Barry Levinson.

3. Marlon Humphrey leads the NFL with four forced fumbles. The Ravens defense was opportunistic in season 2020, forcing at least one takeaway in every game during a streak of 19 games stretching back to 2019. The primary robber of offenses in 2020 has been Marlon Humphrey, who leads the NFL with four forced fumbles. Humphrey has seven forced fumbles since entering the NFL in 2017, just one behind Malcolm Jenkins for the most by a defensive back in that span.

4. Through the first six games of season 2020, Baltimore quarterback Lamar Jackson has tossed ten touchdown passes and two interceptions. In 37 career games, Jackson has thrown 52 touchdowns. Jackson's touchdown strike to Nick Boyle against the Eagles on Sunday moved him out of a tie with Vinny Testaverde for the second most scoring passes in team history.

Jackson only trails Joe Flacco now, with Flacco finishing his Ravens stint with 212 touchdowns.

5. The Ravens defense blitzed heavily in 2019 but was still only able to post 37 quarterback sacks across the whole season. They are still among the league's most blitz-happy teams in 2020, sending extra rushers at a 36.8% rate. But now they are getting to the quarterback, with 22 sacks so far. Off-season acquisition Calais Campbell leads the way with 4.0.

6. Tight end Mark Andrews scored 10 receiving touchdowns in 2019 and has shown a similar appetite for the end zone in 2020. Andrews has five touchdowns after six games, giving him 18 scores in his career.

7. Andrews is locked in a four-way tie for the fourth-most receiving touchdowns in franchise history. The other players with 18 career scores are Qadry Ismail, Michael Jackson, and Derrick Alexander.

8. The first logo of the team came under dispute when Frederick Bouchat contested that it was his design. Ultimately, the courts awarded the rights to Bouchat, but without any monetary damages payable by the team. As a result, three new designs were voted upon by fans, and with a slight modification by Art Modell in the end, the new logo was ready to roll out. For those wondering, Modell wanted the letter "B" in the final logo, and thus it was superimposed on the Raven's head.

C. Answer keys

1. C	20. D	39. C	58. B	77. B
2. D	21. A	40. C	59. B	78. C
3. B	22. C	41. D	60. D	79. B
4. D	23. C	42. C	61. A	80. B
5. C	24. D	43. B	62. C	81. A
6. D	25. C	44. B	63. A	82. C
7. C	26. A	45. A	64. B	83. B
8. C	27. A	46. B	65. C	84. C
9. B	28. A	47. C	66. C	85. B
10. C	29. D	48. B	67. A	86. B
11. D	30. B	49. C	68. A	87. C
12. D	31. C	50. D	69. D	88. A
13. B	32. D	51. D	70. C	89. A
14. D	33. B	52. B	71. A	90. A
15. A	34. A	53. D	72. A	91. B
16. C	35. B	54. C	73. A	92. A
17. D	36. C	55. D	74. C	93. C
18. C	37. D	56. D	75. B	94. C
19. A	38. C	57. C	76. D	95. C

What do you love about the Baltimore Ravens?

Why?

....

....

....

....

....

....

....

....

....

....

....

....

....

Tell us about your favorite Ravens player!

Share photos of your Ravens' game

----- THE END -----

Made in the USA
Middletown, DE
08 December 2021

54611528R00057